the book of
CHANUKAH

poems, riddles, stories, songs and things to do.

by EDYTHE and SOL SCHARFSTEIN

Illustrated by

EZEKIEL SCHLOSS and ARNOLD LOBEL

SECOND REVISED EDITION

LIBRARY OF CONGRESS CATALOG—NUMBER 59-9971

Copyright 1950, 1953, 1959

KTAV PUBLISHING HOUSE INC.

"Wake up, children," called Mother. Joel sat up in bed and rubbed his eyes. All at once he remembered. "Today is Chanukah!" he cried. He jumped out of bed and ran into his sister Riva's room. "Get up, sleepyhead, get up! Don't you know today's the Chanukah party?"

Both children dressed quickly and ran downstairs. Mother had a nice hot breakfast ready for them. When Joel and Riva finished their milk, they asked, "May we go to Grandfather's house now?"

"Not yet!" said Mother. "First we must wrap our Chanukah gifts." Riva ran quickly for the Chanukah paper and seals, while Joel brought a tower of presents to the table. Then Mother helped them wrap the gifts.

Soon they heard a car stop in front of the house. It was Father waiting to take the family to the party.

Joel and Riva raced to the car. The whole family piled into the big car and away they went. They all sang Chanukah songs as they rolled along.

It was a cold, snowy day, but the sun was bright and warm. Before long, they reached Grandfather's house. Riva saw it first. "Hurrah!" she cried. "I see Grandfather's house!" "So do I!" said Joel.

When the car stopped, they tumbled out and ran up the walk.
The door of the house opened.

There stood Grandfather and Grandmother. How happy they were to see their grandchildren! "Happy Chanukah," cried Riva and Joel as they ran up the walk. "Happy Chanukah," said Grandmother and Grandfather. "Come right in and join the party."

THE DRAYDEL

Chanukah is here today;
So with *draydel* we will play.
Spin, spin, spin —
Then count your score.
"*Gimmel*" means
You get some more.

There were many people inside the house. Aunt Marcy and Uncle Phil had already come. Aunt Rachel and Uncle Bernie were there, too. And of course all the cousins were there — Ralph and Alan, Nancy and Wendy, and Vicky, Cindy, and Kit.

From the kitchen came the snap-crackle and pop of frying latkes.

The latkes seemed to be saying, "Happy Chanukah" as they sizzled and crackled in the pan.

And what fun the children were having! Grandfather sat on the floor and showed the children how to play the draydel game.

There was a lot of fun and a lot of noise, but nobody seemed to mind. Everyone was having such a good time!

Meanwhile, Grandmother had set the table. At one end stood a large platter filled with delicious Chanukah cookies. At the other end, was a huge bowl piled high with a mountain of golden brown latkes. My, how fast the food kept disappearing!

The children ate until they could eat no more. Finally Riva said, "Grandfather, please tell us the story of Chanukah."

"First," said Grandfather, "We must light the Menorah." Everyone gathered around the beautiful Menorah.

LATKES

Latkes, latkes, yum— yum— yum!
Don't you wish that you had some?
Latkes, latkes; they taste fine!
Oh, I could eat them all the time!

Grandfather lit the Shammos, and with it lit the first yellow candle. Here is the blessing he said:

I praise God, who is Lord and King over all, who has commanded us to light the Chanukah candles.

בָּרוּךְ אַתָּה יְיָ, אֱלֹהֵינוּ מֶלֶךְ הָעוֹלָם, אֲשֶׁר קִדְּשָׁנוּ בְּמִצְוֹתָיו וְצִוָּנוּ לְהַדְלִיק נֵר שֶׁל חֲנֻכָּה.

Then Grandfather recited another blessing:

I praise God, who is Lord and King over all, who performed miracles for the Maccabees at this time of year.

בָּרוּךְ אַתָּה יְיָ, אֱלֹהֵינוּ מֶלֶךְ הָעוֹלָם, שֶׁעָשָׂה נִסִּים לַאֲבוֹתֵינוּ, בַּיָּמִים הָהֵם בַּזְּמַן הַזֶּה.

Everyone said "Amen."

"There is one blessing we say tonight because it is the first night of Chanukah" said Grandfather.

I praise God, who is Lord and King over all, who watched over us throughout the year and helped us reach this happy holiday.

בָּרוּךְ אַתָּה יְיָ, אֱלֹהֵינוּ מֶלֶךְ הָעוֹלָם, שֶׁהֶחֱיָנוּ וְקִיְּמָנוּ, וְהִגִּיעָנוּ לַזְּמַן הַזֶּה.

Then they all sang the beautiful Chanukah hymn, Rock of Ages.

Joel and Riva sang the loudest because they had been practising the song for weeks.

CHANUKAH

T'was the first night of *Chanukah*,
And down from the shelf,
I took my *menorah*
All by myself.
Two yellow candles my Mom gave to me
To place in the *Menorah* very carefully.
I lit first the *shammos*—
The flame was so red.
Then, kindling the other,
The *brochoh* I said.

Then Joel stood up and said, "I know a Chanukah poem. It is called the 'Chanukah' . . . . . Would you like to hear it?" Everyone listened to Joel as he recited the poem.

"And now," said Grandfather, "let's all sit on the floor and I'll tell you the story of Chanukah."

Many years ago, a wicked Syrian king, named Antiochus, captured the land of Israel. He ordered the Jews to give up their religion and to worship his stone idols. All who refused to obey the King's command were put to death.

In the city of Modin, there lived an old priest whose name was Mattathias the Hasmonean. He had five sons, each one stronger and taller than the other.

One day, Antiochus sent an officer to Modin to build an idol in the market place. When it was finished, the officer ordered everyone in the city to gather around it.

When everyone had gathered around the idol, the officer turned to Mattathias and commanded him to bow down to the stone god.

But Mattathias turned to the officer and said, "Neither I nor my sons nor
any faithful Hebrew will ever worship any idols."

The Syrian officer then called for a volunteer. When one Hebrew stepped forward, Mattathias lunged at the traitor and with one stroke of his knife killed him. He then ran up to the officer and killed him too.

Mattathias then leaped to the top of the altar and shouted, "All those who are faithful to the Lord, follow me."

Mattathias, his five sons and all the able-bodied men in the village, fled to the mountains. As more and more men joined them, they organized a Jewish army.

At first the Jews hid in the mountains and attacked only small groups of soldiers. As they grew stronger, they captured whole towns and started to drive the Syrians out of Israel. Never did men fight more bravely against such odds.

One day Mattathias called his five sons together and said, "My sons, I am dying. After I am gone, you must continue to fight until all the Syrians are driven from the land of Israel. Judah the Maccabee will lead you to victory." Then Mattathias closed his eyes.

Judah took his father's place as Commander-in-chief of the Hebrew army. He continued the successful fight against the Syrians and defeated them many times.

Antiochus became very angry. He gathered a large army with which to defeat the Maccabeans. But with the help of God, the determined little army defeated the Syrians and captured Jerusalem.

Afterwards they marched to the Temple and smashed the idols the Syrians had put there. When they had cleaned and repaired the Temple, everyone came to celebrate the "rededication."

The High Priest could find only one small flask of Holy Oil with which to light the menorah. This was just enough oil to burn for one day. But a great miracle happened! Much to everyone's amazement, the little flask of oil burned for eight days and nights. Because of this miracle we celebrate Chanukah for eight days.

"That was a wonderful story," said Joel breathlessly. "Could you please tell us the story about Hannah and her seven sons?"

"Of course!" answered Grandfather.

During the rule of Antiochus, there lived a good Jewish woman named Hannah. She had seven sons. One day, a Syrian soldier found her observing the Sabbath. He brought her and her seven sons before the King, who ordered them to bow down to his idols. Antiochus spoke to each of the sons, from the eldest to the youngest, but they refused to bow down.

When Antiochus came to the youngest child, he dropped his ring so that it fell right at the feet of the Syrian idol. But, young as the child was, he knew that the King was trying to trick him into bowing down to the idol. So he, too, refused. The angry King then ordered Hannah and her sons put to death.

Grandfather finished telling the story of Hannah. Then he stood, his hands behind his back. With a jolly smile he asked, "Are you ready for a surprise?" The children squealed with delight.

"We know what it is", said Joel. "It's Chanukah gelt." Then Grandfather gave each child a shiny silver dollar.

SURPRISE!

Packages and packages
With Chanukah surprises —
Planes, trains, bikes and dolls,
And toys in all shapes and sizes.

Just then, Grandmother and all the aunts and all the uncles bustled into the room, their arms overflowing with presents. There were gifts for everyone.

Joel and Riva opened their packages as fast as their little fingers could work. How excited Joel was when he opened one package and found a "Big League" bat and ball! And you can imagine how happy Riva was with her beautiful new doll.

TOYS

Around the menorah
  Are presents and toys
For all the little girls
  And all the little boys.
There's a giant teddy bear
  And a tractor red,
A green racing car
  And a shiny yellow sled.
There are blocks and dolls
  And drums that go boom.
There's a train and a bike
  And a plane that goes zoom.

Of course there were many other gifts for Joel and Riva, as well as for all the other children.

Grandfather and Grandmother told the children that there were some more presents hidden about the house. What fun the children had hunting for them!

The afternoon went by quickly. Soon it was time to go home. Grandfather played one last draydel game with the children. Then they all thanked Grandfather and Grandmother for the wonderful Chanukah party and started for home.

Joel and Riva were so tired, they slept all the way. When the car finally stopped at their front door, the children awoke with a start.

"Mother," said Riva, "can't we have Chanukah every day?"
"No, not every day," laughed Mother. "Purim isn't so far away, and then we'll have another party."

That night Joel and Riva went to sleep and dreamed of dancing draydels and flying menorahs.

LITTLE YOMO

1. Once upon a time there was a little Israeli boy named Little Yomo.

2. For Chanukah, his mother made him a little blue skull cap and a beautiful new sailor suit.

3. His father went to the store, and bought him a beautiful red draydel and a lovely pair of new white shoes. And wasn't little Yomo grand!

4. So Yomo took his red draydel, put on his new clothes and went for a walk in the fields. By and by, he met a duck.

5. The duck said to him, "Little Yomo, give me your beautiful red draydel!" And Little Yomo said, "Oh! Please, Mr. Duck, don't take my draydel, and I'll give you my beautiful new sailor suit."
So the duck said, "Very well. I won't take your draydel this time, but you must give me your new sailor suit."

6. The duck put on Little Yomo's new suit and went away saying, "Now I'm the grandest duck on the whole farm."

7. Little Yomo walked on. And by and by, he met a goat. The goat said to him, "Little Yomo, give me your red draydel."
And Little Yomo said, "Oh! Please, Mr. Goat, don't take my red draydel and I'll give you my beautiful blue skull cap."

8. So the goat said, "Very well. I won't take your draydel this time, but you must give me your pretty blue skull cap."
The goat put on Little Yomo's blue skull cap between his two horns and went away saying, "Now I'm the grandest goat on the whole farm."

9. Little Yomo went on. And by and by he met a chicken. The chicken said to him, "Little Yomo, give me your red draydel."
And Little Yomo said, "Oh! Please, Mr. Chicken, don't take my red draydel and I'll give you my new shoes."

10. So the chicken said, "Very well, I won't take your draydel this time, but you must give me your new shoes."
The chicken put on Little Yomo's new white shoes and went away saying, "Now I'm the grandest chicken on the whole farm."

11. Little Yomo went on, and by and by he met a cow. The cow said to him, "Little Yomo, give me your red draydel."

12. And Little Yomo said, "Oh! Please, Mr. Cow, don't take my Chanukah draydel. I have something special for you at home. If you'll wait right here, I'll run home and bring it to you."
But the cow said, "Oh! no! I want your red draydel."

13. And Little Yomo said, "A draydel isn't a good toy for a cow. You can't even spin it!" But the cow said, "I could tie a knot in my tail and carry it as an umbrella."

14. So poor Little Yomo's Chanukah draydel ended upon the tail of the cow, who went away saying, "Now I'm the grandest cow on the whole farm."

15. Poor Little Yomo went away crying because the animals had taken all his new clothes and his beautiful red Chanukah draydel.

16. Soon he heard a terrible noise that sounded like animals fighting. Little Yomo was frightened.
He quickly climbed a palm tree to see what the noise was all about.

17. From the top of the tree, Little Yomo saw all the farm animals fighting and arguing about which of them was the grandest animal in the whole farm.

18. The animals got so excited that they took off all their new clothes and began to fight around the very tree where Little Yomo was hiding.

19. The animals took hold of each other's tails, and they found themselves in a ring around the tree.

20. They ran around the tree, and they ran faster and faster and faster, till they all just melted away. Soon there was nothing left but a great big circle of butter around the foot of the tree.

21. When the animals had disappeared, Little Yomo climbed down from the tree, put on his new clothes, grabbed his red draydel, and ran home.

22. Now Yomo's father was just coming home from work with a great big pail in his hand. When he saw the butter, he put it all in the pail and took it home to Little Yomo's mother.

23. When Little Yomo's mother saw the butter, she said, "Now I'll grate some potatoes and make latkes for Chanukah."

24. And that night, after Little Yomo and his father blessed the Chanukah candles, everyone ate a big plate of delicious Chanukah latkes, fried in the very butter Father had brought home.

WHAT IS IT?

22 • 23 •

1 • 6 • 7 • 12 • 13 • 18 • 19 •   26 • 27 • 32 • 33 • 38 • 39 • 44 •

20 • 21 • 24 • 25 •

17 • 16 • 29 • 28 •

14 • 15 • 30 • 31 •

11 • 10 • 35 • 34 •

8 • 9 • 36 • 37 •

5 • 4 • 41 • 40 •

2 • 3 • 42 • 43 •

Follow the numbers and draw a
line from number to number,
until you have completed the
whole picture.

DRAYDEL GAME

This game can be played for nuts, candies, cookies, toothpicks, etc. Any number of children or adults can participate.

The rules of the game are:

1. Everyone must start with the same number of nuts, cookies, etc.

2. To start the game, each player puts one nut, etc., into the "Kitty".

3. Everyone takes a turn at spinning the draydel.

4. The player has to do what the draydel tells him - either take, put in, or do nothing.

NUN - Nisht - nothing. This means you do nothing.

GIMMEL — Gantz — all. Take all in the "Kitty."

HAY — Half — Take half of the "Kitty."

SHEEN — Shtell — Tzu — add. Add a nut etc., into the "Kitty."

Play until one person has all the nuts.

CHANUKAH DICTIONARY

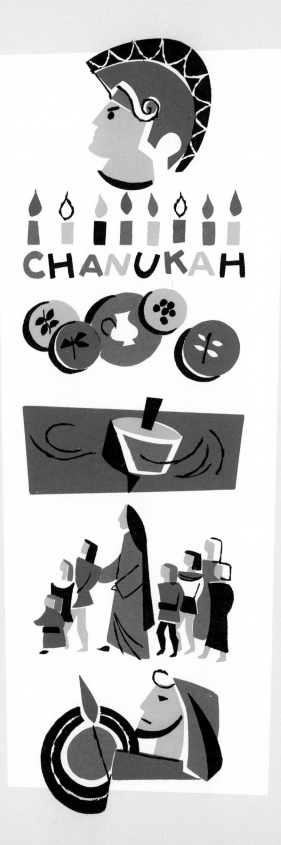

ANTIOCHUS—
    cruel King of the Syrians.

CHANUKAH—
    also called Feast of Lights. It celebrates the victory of the Maccabees over the wicked Syrians. At this time we light our Menorah for eight days, one for the first night and an extra one for each additional night.

CHANUKAH GELT—
    traditional money gift given to children on Chanukah.

DRAYDEL—
    a four-sided top used on Chanukah. Each side has a different Hebrew letter. Nun, Gimmel, Hay, Sheen. This stands for NES GODOL HAWYAW SHOM, which means "A great miracle happened there."

HANNAH—
    Jewess who defied the Syrians.

JUDAH THE MACCABEE—
    son of Mattathias who led the fight against the Syrians.

MACCABEES—

    Hebrew soldiers who fought the Syrians. Named after their leader, Judah the Maccabee.

MATTATHIAS the Hasmoean—

    Priest who started the revolt against the Syrians.

MENORAH—

    Chanukah candle holder.

SHAMMOS—

    Helper-Candle used to light all the other candles.

LATKES—

    potato pancakes. Traditional Chanukah delicacy.

MAOZ TZUR—

    Traditional Chanukah song, "Rock of Ages."

How many mistakes can you find in this Chanukah picture?